This cool-a-ra Annual 2005

belongs to

....

Find and Match the Musical Instruments

The Tweenies are pretending to play their favourite musical instruments. The instruments are hidden on some of the pages in this annual. Can you find them, and match one to each of the Tweenies? The answer is on page 61.

BBC CHILDREN'S BOOKS
Published by the Penguin Group
Penguin Books Ltd, 80 Strand, London WC2R 0RL, England
Penguin Books Australia Ltd, 250 Camberwell Road, Camberwell, Victoria 3124, Australia
Published by BBC Children's Books, 2004
Text and design © BBC Children's Books
2 4 6 8 10 9 7 5 3 1
Text by Sally Foord-Kelcey
Illustrations by Stephanie Longfoot, Magic Island and Bill Titcombe
Photography on pages 20-21, 26-27, 38-39 and 50-51 by Christopher Baines
With thanks to Amelia, Emma, Michael, Hannah and Henry
Design by Matt Hayes
Tweenies © 1998 BBC
Tweenies © 1999 BBC Worldwide Ltd
Tweenies is produced by Tell-Tale Productions for the BBC.
Printed in Belgium
ISBN 0563 49283 X

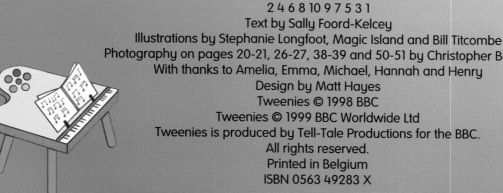

Tweenie clock – where will it stop?

Boom Boom
Mime the actions and sing along with the Tweenies

We can play on the big base drum
And this is the way we do it.
Boom, boom, boom goes the big base drum
And that's the way we do it.

We can play on the violin
And this is the way we do it.
Fiddle diddle dee goes the violin
And that's the way we do it.

We can play on the slide trombone
And this is the way we do it.
Sli-de goes the slide trombone
And that's the way we do it.

We can play on the base guitar
And this is the way we do it.
Neeou neeou neeou goes the base guitar
And that's the way we do it.

We can play on the Doodles dog
And this is the way we do it.
Ruff, ruff, ruff goes the Doodles dog
And that's the way we do it.

We can do them all at once
And this is the way we do it.
Boom, boom, boom, fiddle dee dee, sli-de,
neeou, neeou, neeou, ruff, ruff, ruff
And that's the way we do it.

7

Milo's Music Machine

One day, the Tweenies were talking about musical instruments.
"I can play a drum," Jake told the others. "Boom!"
"I can play a drum and a rattler," said Fizz. "Boom! Rattle!"
"Well, I can play a drum and a rattler and a tooter," boasted Bella.
"Boom! Rattle! Toot!"

"I can play everything!" giggled Milo. "Boomers, rattlers, tooters, crashers, clackers..."
"Bet you can't play them all at once," said Bella.
"Bet I can!" Milo replied, because he'd just had an idea. He was going to make a music machine.

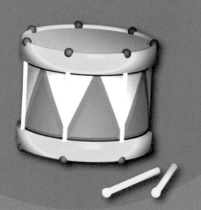

8

Max was clearing out a cupboard when Milo came along with a wheelbarrow.

"Can I have those saucepan lids to make a crasher for my music machine?" asked Milo.

"Help yourself," said Max.

Milo banged the lids together.

Crash!

Jake was playing in the sandpit when Milo came along with the wheelbarrow. He had hung the lids from one of the handles.

"Can I have two of your bricks to make a clacker for my music machine?" asked Milo.

"Take what you want," said Jake, "but don't spoil my sandcastle."

Milo banged the bricks and kicked the lids all at once.

Crash!

Clack!

Fizz was gluing a bean and pasta picture when Milo came along with the wheelbarrow.

"Can I have that jar of beans to make a rattler for my music machine?" asked Milo.

"Take what you want," said Fizz, "but don't tread on my picture."

Milo tied the jar of beans to his leg. Then he banged the bricks, kicked the lids and shook the beans, all at once.

Crash! Clack! Rattle!

Bella was making a dinosaur when Milo came along with the wheelbarrow.

"Can I have that tube to make a tooter for my music machine?" Milo asked.

"Hurry up and take what you want," said Bella. "I'm in the middle of a difficult bit."

Milo banged the bricks, kicked the lids, shook the beans and blew into the tube, all at once.

Crash!
Rattle!
Toot!

Clack!

Judy was tidying up when Milo came along with the wheelbarrow. "Can I have that box to make a boomer for my music machine?" asked Milo.

"That sounds fun," said Judy. "Take what you want."

Milo put the box in the wheelbarrow. Then he banged the bricks, kicked the lids, shook the beans and blew into the tube, all at once.

Clack! Crash! Rattle! Toot!

Everyone came to watch Milo.

"Tee hee!" giggled Fizz. "Milo can't make his music machine work."

"Milo can't play everything all at once," teased Bella.

Doodles was laughing so much that he rolled over and waved his legs in the air. That gave Milo an idea...

11

He lay on his back next to the wheelbarrow. Then he banged the bricks, kicked the lids, shook the beans, blew into the tube and thumped the box with his foot – all at once.

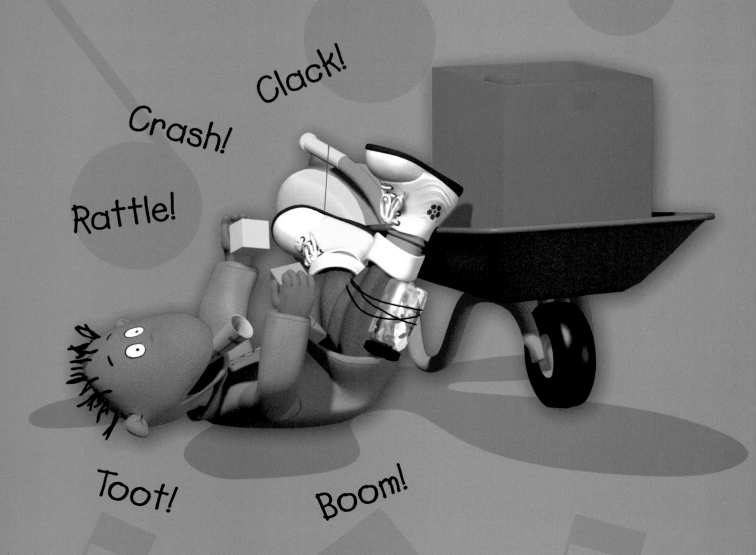

Crash!

Clack!

Rattle!

Toot!

Boom!

The End

Colour by Numbers

messy time

Crash! Here's Milo with his music machine. He's banging two lids together. Colour in the picture, using the numbers and the colour chart to help you.

Odd One Out

One day, Judy showed the Tweenies an odd one out game on the computer.

"It's easy to play," she explained. "You just have to pick out something that doesn't belong with the rest of the group. Look."

She pointed to pictures on the screen of three sheep and a cow.

"The cow's the odd one out," said Bella, "because the rest are sheep."

When they'd finished playing on the computer, the Tweenies went and looked in the toy box for something else to play with. Bella and Fizz found dolls and Jake found a train, but Milo couldn't find anything he liked.

"That makes Milo the odd one out," Fizz giggled.

"Yes, it does," said Milo. "Let's play an odd one out game. We'll call this red hat the odd one out hat, and I'll wear it first."

Next, the Tweenies went outside and tried to bounce balls with one hand. They could all do it except Jake, but he didn't mind a bit.

"I'm the odd one out," he laughed, "so I can wear the red hat."

Bella said she wanted to dress up as a beautiful fairy.

"You always dress up as a fairy, Bella," Milo told her. "Why don't you try something different?"

"I've just had a brilliant idea," she cried. "Let's all dress up in secret and surprise each other."

"Oh, I love surprises," said Fizz.

Milo stepped though the surprise curtains first. He was dressed as a caterpillar. Jake followed. He was a spider.

"We're both bugs!" Milo told Jake.

Then Fizz arrived. She was a butterfly.

"Look! Fizz is a bug, too," Jake pointed out.

When the curtains opened again, there was Bella, dressed as Goldilocks.

"Oh," said Fizz. "You'll have to wear the red hat, Bella."

"Why?" Bella replied crossly. "It won't look nice with my costume."

"Because you're the odd one out!" cried Fizz. "We're all bugs except you."

When it was news time, the Tweenies told Judy all about their odd one out game.

"It's not fair," Fizz complained. "I'm the only one who hasn't worn the red hat."

"That makes you the odd one out," said Milo. "You can wear it now!"

The End

Odd One Out
Colour In

Fizz is going to paint three of her drawings pink and one blue, but she can't decide which will be the odd one out. Help Fizz choose, and then colour in the picture.

17

Odd One Out Fun

Here are some of the odd one out games the Tweenies played on the computer. Can you spot the odd one out in each game?

I know! I know!

Um!

I wish I could live there!

One, two, three...!

Woof woof!

Odd One Out
Star Mobile

Fizz loves stars! Make this pretty mobile, and ask your friends to spot the odd star out.

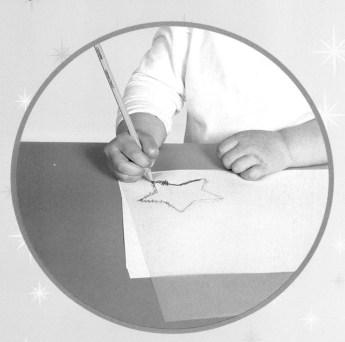

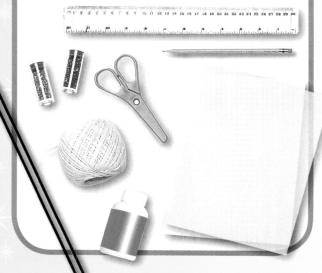

1 Place the tracing paper over the star template and copy over the lines in pencil. Turn the tracing paper over and scribble over the lines on the back. Now place the tracing paper the right way up over the white card. Pressing hard with the pencil, draw over the lines to make a star shape.

Template

2 Make four star shapes on the card, and cut them out.

3 Spread glue on one side of the stars.

4 Sprinkle glitter on the glued areas of the stars. When the first side is dry, turn each star over and do the same on the back. Make one star the odd one out by using different coloured glitter.

5 Cross the sticks over each other, and ask a grown-up to help you tie them together in the middle with string. Make sure there is an extra long piece of string to hang your mobile from.

6 Cut four 30cm pieces of string. Glue one end of each piece of string to a star. Tie the other ends to the ends of the sticks.

Now you can hang up your fab-a-rooney mobile.

21

Who's the Odd One Out?

The Tweenies have made up a song about being the odd one out. Colour in the pictures as you sing along.

Listen to our little song.
It doesn't matter if you don't belong.
So don't worry if you have to shout,
"Looks like I'm the odd one out!"

Every day, whatever you play,
Someone's not going to fit.
So if it's you, don't feel blue.
It doesn't matter one little bit!

Listen to our little song.
It doesn't matter if you don't belong.
So don't worry if you have to shout,
"Looks like I'm the odd one out!"

It really isn't all that bad.
Don't let it make you feel mad.
So when it's you, just laugh and say,
"I'm going to find something else to play!"

Yeah, listen to our little song.
It doesn't matter if you don't belong.
We want you all to sing and shout,
"I LIKE BEING THE ODD ONE OUT!"

Which Tweenie is the odd one out?

23

Funnyrooney Animal Jokes

How do snails make their shells so shiny?
They use snail varnish.

What do you call a bear with no socks on?
Bare-foot.

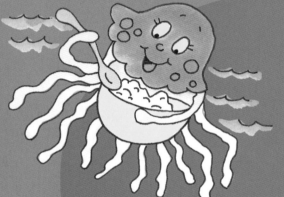

What kind of fish goes
well with ice-cream?
Jellyfish.

What do you call a cow eating
grass in a garden?
A lawn mooer.

Where do sheep go to get haircuts?
To the baa baa shop.

How do you start a teddy bear race?
Ready, teddy, go!

What do you call an elephant that flies?
A jumbo jet.

Why do bees have sticky hair?
Because they use honey combs.

Why does a hummingbird hum?
Because it doesn't know the words.

What do toads drink?
Croaka-cola!

What do you get if you cross a tiger with a kangaroo?
A stripy jumper.

What do you get when you put a fish and an elephant together?
Swimming trunks.

Making Music

Milo loves music! Make a Twang Twang Box Guitar and a Bean Shaky Shaker, and play and sing your favourite songs with your friends.

Twang Twang Box Guitar

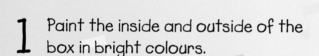

You will need:
A shoebox without its lid
Paint
A paintbrush
4 elastic bands
A grown-up to help

1 Paint the inside and outside of the box in bright colours.

2 When the paint is dry, put the four elastic bands around the box, leaving spaces between them.

Bean Shaky Shaker

You will need:
2 paper cups
Dried beans
Sticky tape
Paint
A paint brush
A grown-up to help

1 Paint the outside of the two paper cups.

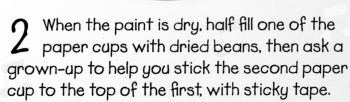

2 When the paint is dry, half fill one of the paper cups with dried beans, then ask a grown-up to help you stick the second paper cup to the top of the first, with sticky tape.

Your Twang Twang Box Guitar and Bean Shaky Shaker are ready to play!

Caterpillar Surprise

One day, Max and the Tweenies were watching a programme about bugs on the telly.

"There's a spider chasing a fly," said Milo. "Spiderooney!"

"What's that creepy-crawly?" asked Jake, pointing to something stripy on a leaf.

"It's a caterpillar," Max told him.

"I can see two ladybirds," said Fizz, pointing to a pair of red and black spotty bugs. "I love ladybirds!"

Bella wanted to see butterflies, but none were shown.

"Why don't we go and look for butterflies in the garden?" she suggested, when they had finished watching telly.

"Good idea," said the others.

But there were no butterflies in the garden. Then Jake saw something on a leaf.

"It looks like a jelly bean," he said.

"It's not a jelly bean," said Bella. "It's a cocoon. There's a caterpillar inside it. When it grows up it turns into something wonderful."

"What happens next?" Milo asked. "Does the caterpillar wake up?"

"Something like that," said Max. "Let me explain. First, a baby caterpillar grows from an egg. When the caterpillar gets bigger, it changes into something else."

"I know," said Bella. "The caterpillar changes into a..."

"Shhh, Bella!" said Max suddenly. "Let's keep the next bit a secret so the change is a surprise."

"Can we take the cocoon inside?" asked Fizz.

"I think we should leave it here where it belongs," Max replied. "We can come and see it everyday."

The Tweenies went off to find different things to do.
Jake painted a picture of a caterpillar, and Fizz drew a ladybird.

Bella read a book about butterflies.

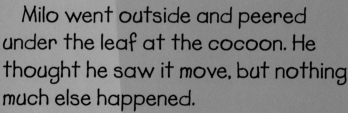

Milo went outside and peered under the leaf at the cocoon. He thought he saw it move, but nothing much else happened.

"When are we going to get our surprise?" he asked.

Then Fizz went outside to see if anything had happened to the cocoon, but it looked exactly the same.

"Where's the surprise?" she thought.

Later, Jake went outside to see if the caterpillar had woken up. But all he could see was the little cocoon dangling from the leaf.

"It's not much of a surprise," he thought.

Only Bella stayed away from the garden. She knew that you had to be patient if you wanted to enjoy this surprise. She carried on reading her book. It had some lovely pictures in it.

The next day and the day after that, there was no sign of the caterpillar waking up. Then, early one morning, Max called the Tweenies into the garden. The cocoon had broken open. The outsides of the caterpillar's silky coat had fallen to the ground. Something small and crumpled held on tightly to the leaf. Then it slowly opened up...

31

"It's a flutterby!" cried Jake.

"You mean a butterfly," said Fizz.

"Wow! What a great surprise," said Milo.

"It's beautiful," said Bella.

The butterfly stretched its wings and fluttered away, over their heads and up into the sky.

"Bye-bye, butterfly," called the Tweenies, and waved goodbye.

The End

Join the Dots
and Colour In

messy time

Bella has seen a beautiful butterfly. Join the dots so you can see it, too. Then colour in the picture.

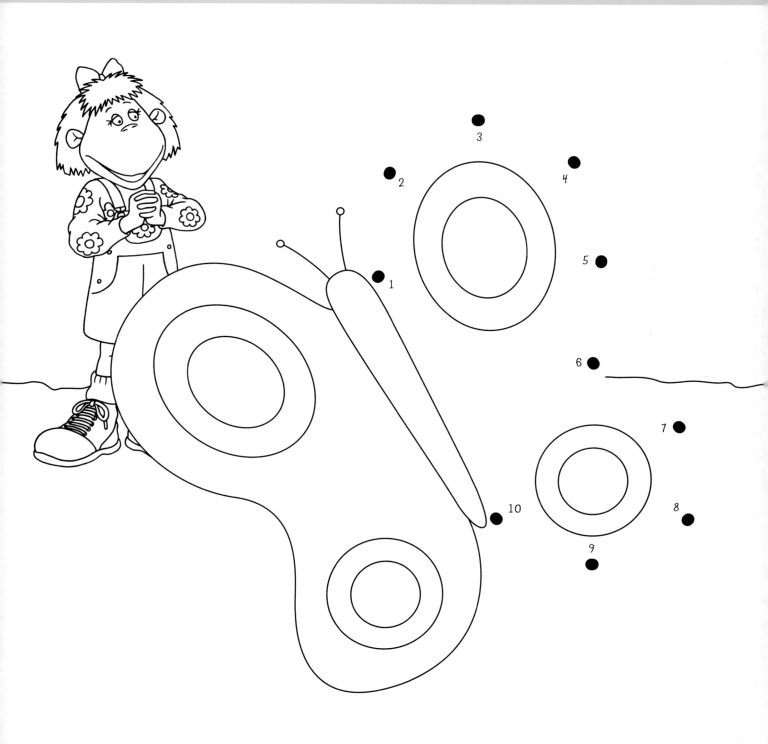

Caterpillar Walking

Max and Bella know a song about caterpillars.
Copy their movements and sing along with them.

Caterpillar walking
Up and down the trees.

Caterpillar munching
On the tasty leaves.

Caterpillar hiding,
Nowhere to be found.

Caterpillar sleeping,
Safe and sound.

Caterpillar waking,
Looks up to the sky.

Opens out her wings, and becomes
a butterfly!

Butterfly House

One day, Max took Bella to a butterfly house, where they looked at beautiful butterflies. Bella learnt how a caterpillar turns into a butterfly.

1) The adult butterfly lays eggs.

2) The eggs grow and then hatch open.

3) A tiny caterpillar comes out of the egg.

Count how many of these there are in the big picture.

- ☐ Orange butterflies
- ☐ Yellow butterflies
- ☐ Pink flowers
- ☐ Cocoons

4) The caterpillar eats leaves.

5) The caterpillar spins silk around itself. The silk turns into a hard case called a cocoon.

6) After a few days, the cocoon breaks open and a beautiful butterfly comes out.

Answers: 1 orange butterfly; 2 yellow butterflies; 5 pink flowers; 2 cocoons.

Butterfly Paper Chain

Bella loves butterflies! Make this beautiful paper chain and use it to decorate your wall.

You will need:
An A4 sheet of paper
A pencil
Round-ended scissors
Felt tip pens or
other colouring materials
A grown-up to help

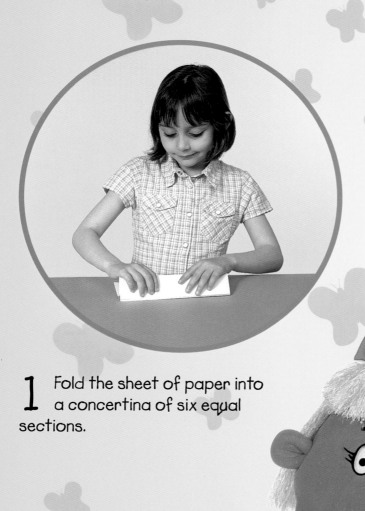

1 Fold the sheet of paper into a concertina of six equal sections.

2 Draw the outline of half a butterfly on the first section. The body should be on the fold and the top wing should disappear off the edge of the paper.

3 Carefully cut along the pencil lines.

4 Now unfold your butterfly paper chain and decorate it using felt tip pens or other colouring materials.

If you want a longer chain, simply make another one and stick them together.

Music Fun

Thump! Thump! Join the dots to see Jake's drum.
Then colour in the picture.

Find the two pictures
of Fizz that are the same.

Can you spot five differences between these two pictures?

Answers: Bella's shoes, pattern on Milo's top, Jake's hair, missing music note and buttons on tape player.

The Wheels
On The Train

This is one of Jake's favourite songs because it is about trains. Act out the words as you sing along with the Tweenies.

The wheels on the train
go round and round,
Round and round,
Round and round.
The wheels on the train
go round and round,
All day long.

The engine on the train
goes chuff, chuff, chuff,
Chuff, chuff, chuff,
Chuff, chuff, chuff.
The engine on the train
goes chuff, chuff, chuff,
All day long.

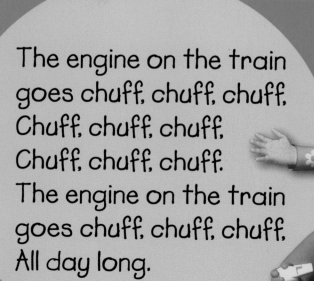

The whistle on the train
goes toot, toot, toot,
Toot, toot, toot,
Toot, toot, toot,
The whistle on the train
goes toot, toot, toot,
All day long.

The people on the train
sway side to side,
Side to side,
Side to side.
The people on the train
sway side to side,
All day long.

The wheels on the train
go round and round,
Round and round,
Round and round.
The wheels on the train
go round and round,
All day long.

Brand New Choo-Choo

One day, Jake lost his train.

"Have you seen my choo-choo?" he asked Fizz.

"No, I haven't," said Fizz. "Let's look for it together."

First they went to the book corner, where Bella was reading.

"Have you seen my choo-choo?" Jake asked her.

"No, I haven't," said Bella. "Where did you last play with it? Were you in the book corner?"

"I don't think so," said Jake, "but sometimes I bring my choo-choo here and look at pictures in the train book."

The train wasn't in the book corner, but Fizz found two coloured pencils under the beanbags.

"You could draw a train," she suggested.

"No, thank you," said Jake. "I just want to find my choo-choo."

"What else do you do with your train?" asked Bella.

"Sometimes I use the bricks to build a bridge for it," Jake replied.

Milo was playing with the bricks.

"Have you seen Jake's train?" Fizz asked him.

"No, but he can play with the rocket I've just built," said Milo.

"No, thank you," said Jake. "I just want to find my choo-choo."

Bella and Fizz tipped up the brick box to see if Jake's train was in there.

They didn't find the train but they found Milo's whistle. Milo started to toot on it very loudly.

"Let's look outside," Bella suggested.

"Sometimes I make hills and tunnels for my choo-choo in the sandpit," said Jake.

There were lots of things in the sandpit, but no train.

"Look," said Bella. "These cotton reels belong in the messy corner. Let's go and put them back."

45

Jake said he sometimes ran his train along the worktop in the messy corner and stopped at the paint pot stations. But the train wasn't there either. Judy wondered what they were doing, so Bella explained.

"And while we were looking for Jake's train we found these pencils and cotton reels," she said, and put them on the table.

Judy gave Jake a hug. Then she said, "Don't worry. I've had an idea."

She found two boxes and a cardboard roll and stuck them together.

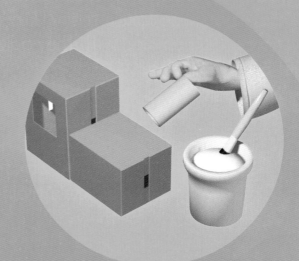

Then she poked the pencils through the boxes, and put the cotton reels and little balls of modelling clay on the ends that stuck out.

Bella and Fizz painted the train bright red, and decorated it with gold stickers.

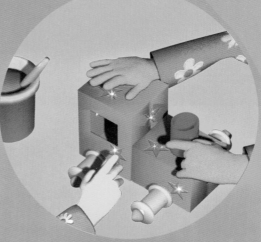

When they had finished, Jake was very pleased.

"A brand new choo-choo! Oh, thank you!"

Toot toot! Milo blew his whistle and the Tweenies set off behind Jake and his brand new choo-choo, pretending to be a train. They ran around, faster and faster, and when they had run out of space indoors they ran outside. The Tweenie train chuffed up the climbing frame steps.

Jake went down first but stopped suddenly at the bottom. The others slid down next and bumped into him.
"Hey," yelled Jake.
"Sorry!" said the others.
"No," laughed Jake. "Look, everyone. Look what I've found!"

It was Jake's train!
"It wasn't lost after all," said Fizz.
"It was just waiting at the station," said Bella.
"Toot toot!" went Milo.
Jake smiled. Now he had two choo-choos to play with.

The End

Search and Colour

Jake is looking for his train.
Help him find it - colour the shapes with a dot, red.
Then colour in the rest of the scene.

49

Choo-Choo Jigsaw

You will need:
Paint
A paintbrush
An A4 sheet of paper
Glue, ruler, a pencil
Card (the same size as the paper)
Round-ended scissors

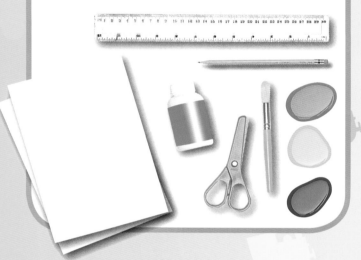

Jake loves trains! Make this choo-choo jigsaw for yourself or as a present for a friend.

1 Paint a picture of a train on the piece of paper.

2 When the picture is dry, spread glue on the back of the paper.

3 Stick the painting onto the card.

4 Draw the pieces of the jigsaw on the back of the card, using a ruler.

5 Cut along the jigsaw lines.

Your choo-choo jigsaw puzzle is ready to solve!

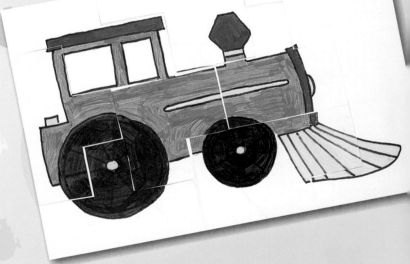

Choo-Choo Fun

Can you draw a train like Jake's? Join the dots. Add three wheels, a round window and a chimney. Then colour in your picture.

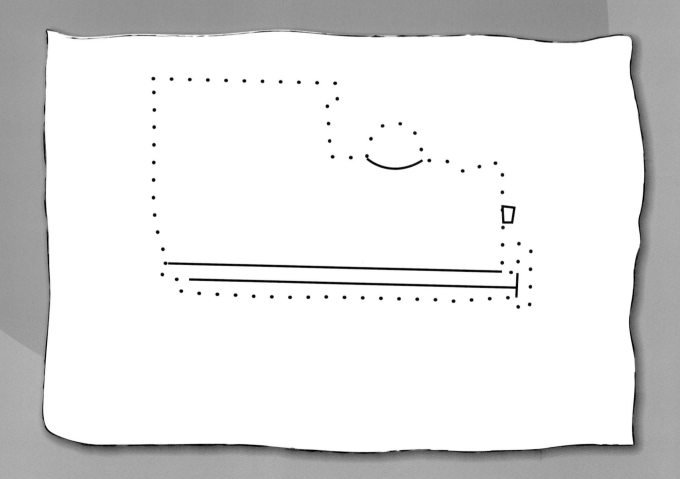

Jake and Fizz are playing trains in the sandpit.
Jake is going to push the train across the sandpit
to Fizz. Can you help him find the way?

Help Jake match the engines to the carriages by
drawing a line between them.

messy time

Colour in the Tweenies

The Tweenies love stories, and so do Doodles and Izzles.
Colour in this picture of them in the book corner
with Judy.

The Da Doo-Wah Woof Song

Here's a chance to make a tiny Tweenies storybook. Cut out the page opposite, follow the step-by-step instructions below, and you will have a book to keep in your pocket and read whenever you want.

1) Cut along the dotted lines. ....

2) Fold the little pages along the folding lines. ----------

3) Put them together in the right page order to make the book.

4) Put an elastic band around the pages to keep them together.

"I'm afraid what you need to dance like Doodles are these," he giggled.

Then he rolled on his back and waved four very big, very clumsy doggy paws in the air.

THE END

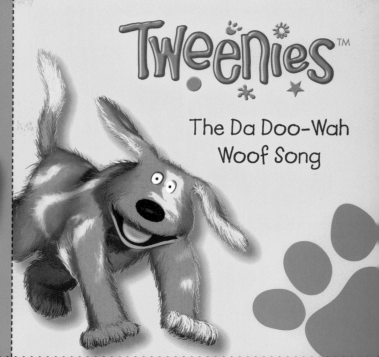

Tweenies™

The Da Doo-Wah Woof Song

Suddenly, Doodles didn't feel tired any more. His paws tapped, his head bobbed... and he started to dance. He was the best dancer the Tweenies had ever seen.

Milo was collecting tins to use as drums in the Tweenie band.

Doodles asked if he could play them in the band.

"Sorry, mate," Milo replied. "Your paws are too big to hold the drum sticks."

Doodles tried to sleep in the playhouse, but a buzzing fly disturbed him. Then he went outside, but it started to rain. So he went back indoors and lay on his beanbag.

Fizz was looking for a costume to wear in the band. Doodles tried to help her.

"Doodles, stop it!" cried Fizz. "You're so clumsy. You're messing things up."

One day, Bella was making a shaker to play in the Tweenie band. Doodles asked if he could shake it in the band.

"Sorry, Doodles," said Bella. "Your paws are too clumsy to hold it."

2

"Oh, Doodles," they said. "We didn't know you could dance. Can you teach us?"

Doodles shook his head.

11

Jake was banging spoons together and humming.

Doodles asked if he could play the spoony thing in the band.

"Sorry, Doodles," said Jake. "Your paws are too clumsy to hold the spoons."

4

Just then, the Tweenie band started to sing, "Doodles is the one we all adore, da doo-wah, woof, da doo-wah, woof!"

9

Poor Doodles went off to find a quiet corner. If no one wanted him, he might as well have a snooze.

6

But it wasn't quiet. The Tweenie band was starting to practise.

7

Colour and Collage Fun

messy time

Fizz and Milo love to sing and dance. Colour in the picture, and stick on glittery bits to make them look like pop stars.

59

What Can You Remember?

Tweenie clock – where will it stop? It's news time! The Tweenies are telling Max and Judy about all the things they have done in this annual. Can you help them to remember?

1) What noise does the violin make in this song?

2) In this story, what did Milo use the wheelbarrow for?

3) Find the odd one out here.

4) What is the answer to this joke?
How do snails make their shells so shiny?

5) When a cocoon breaks open, what comes out?

6) What did Judy make for Jake out of two boxes, one cardboard tube, two pencils, four cotton reels and modelling clay?

7) Who are the Tweenies singing about here?
What is the name
of the song?

Answers to Find and Match the Musical Instruments on page 4: Jake is playing the guitar, which is on page 26; Milo is playing the saxophone, which is on page 41; Bella is playing the violin, which is on page 23 and Fizz is playing the piano, which is on page 56.
Answers to What Can You Remember?: 1) Fiddle diddle dee; 2) A music machine; 3) The pink house; 4) They use snail varnish; 5) A butterfly; 6) A choo-choo; 7) Doodles; The Da Doo-Wah Woof Song.

Quiet and Noisy Board Game

This is a game for two or more players. You will need a die and a counter for each player.

This is your chance to make a lot of noise or keep very quiet! When you land on a song time square you can sing one of the Tweenies' favourite songs. And you can be noisy when you land on some other squares, too. But if you land on an empty square you must keep very quiet, or go back one! So put your counters on the START square, roll the die and get playing!

START

song time

song time

Moo like a cow. Miss a turn.

Make a sound like a fire engine. Move forward 1 square.